The Bored @Work

Pocket **Doodle** Book

Thank you: Miss Boakes, Roland, the
family, Ed and Gizmo, Parker and
Lamy, Chester Floyd Carlson – and you

Published by SevenOaks
20 Mortimer Street
London W1T 3JW

Images copyright © 2009 Ross Adams
Design & layout copyright © 2015 Carlton
  Books Ltd

ISBN 978-1-78177-355-0

10 9 8 7 6 5 4 3 2

Printed and bound by CPI Group (UK) Ltd,
Croydon, CR0 4YY

The images in this book were previously
published in the Bored at Work Doodle Book

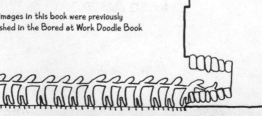

The
Bored
@Work
Pocket Doodle Book

Hundreds of ideas to put you off your daily chores

Rose Adders

SevenOaks

Draw in this book

Colour in the images

Add to the drawings

Stick things in it

Fill the pages with stuff

Cover the pages in
something more interesting

It's your book ... use it!

Getting to know you...

MY NAME IS:

[ ]

BUT THEY CALL ME:

[ ]

I WORK AS A:

[ ]

FOR:

[ ]

WITH:

I LIKE MY JOB BECAUSE:

I WANT TO GET BETTER AT:

Wake up... look in the mirror

THIS IS WHAT I LOOK LIKE:

MY FACE BEFORE LEAVING THE HOUSE:

After your commute to work

MY FACE AT MY DESK:

MY FACE AFTER WORK:

Rate your job satisfaction

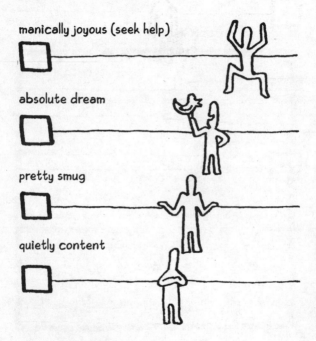

manically joyous (seek help)

absolute dream

pretty smug

quietly content

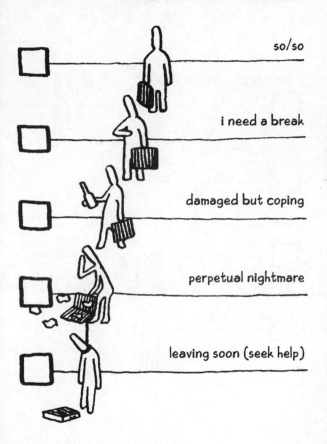

so/so

i need a break

damaged but coping

perpetual nightmare

leaving soon (seek help)

Design your own company logo

Graffiti the walls

Pick a nose...

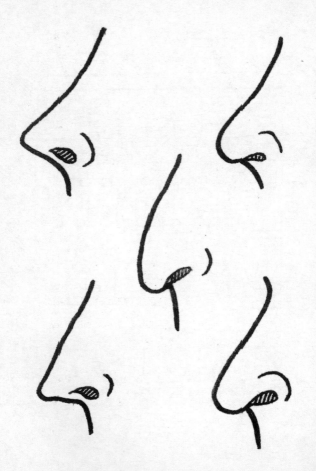

Give these noses an appropriate colour

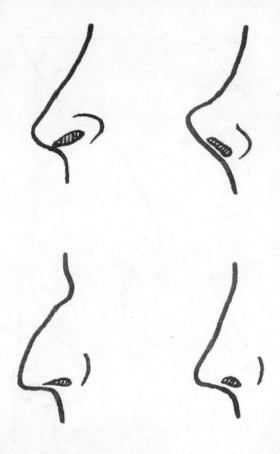

Vandalize the nearest piece of
office art

Career Snakes and Ladders

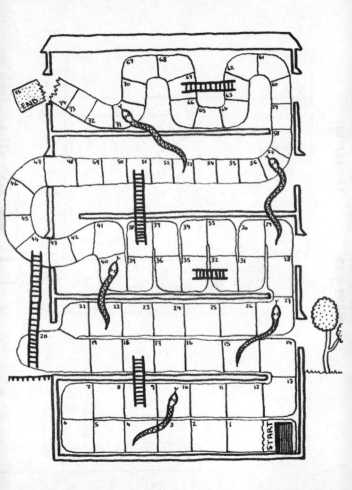

Start a fire and evacuate everyone

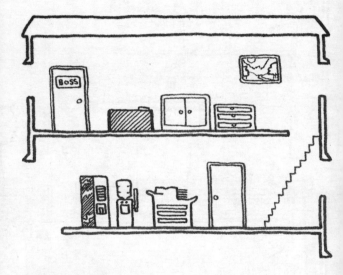

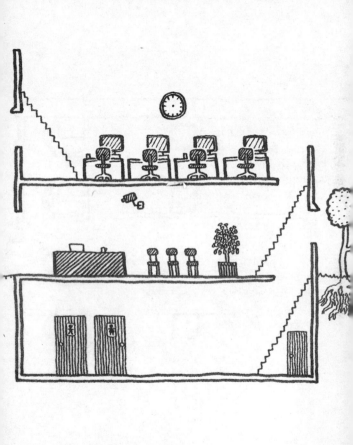

How full is your cup?

bottomless
(seek help) ☐

brimming ☐

plenty left ☐

couple of gulps ☐

realistic –
mid-range ☐

few sips ☐

dregs ☐

kettle on ☐

what cup?
(seek help) ☐

Draw some interesting learning curves

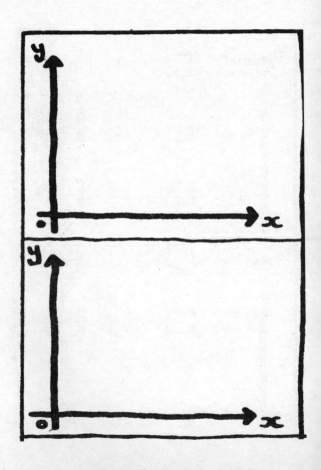

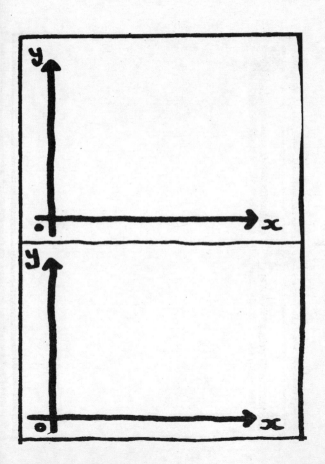

Draw some more interesting
learning curves

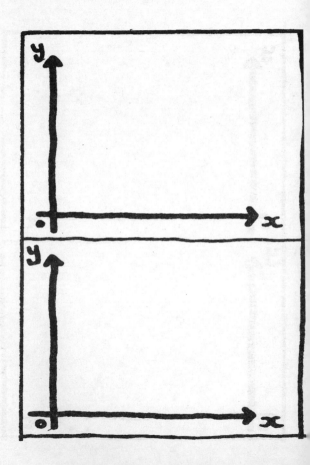

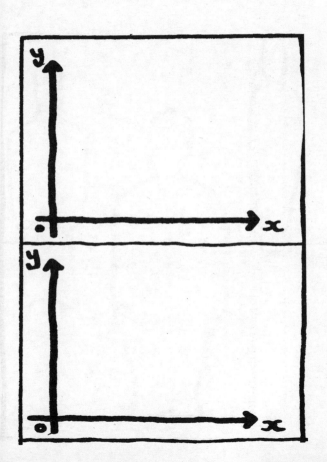

Dress your co-workers for the weekend

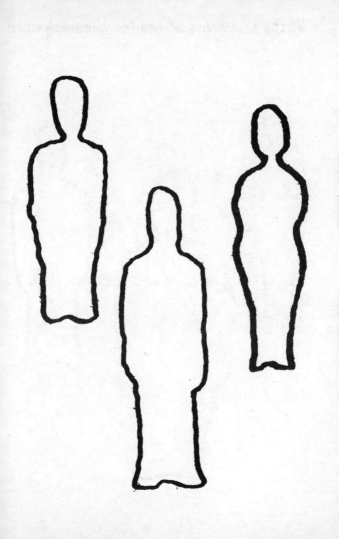

*Sorry to hear
that you are leaving.*

Make a mug-ring galaxy

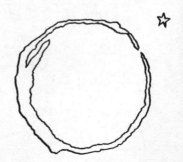

Draw the team dogsbodies

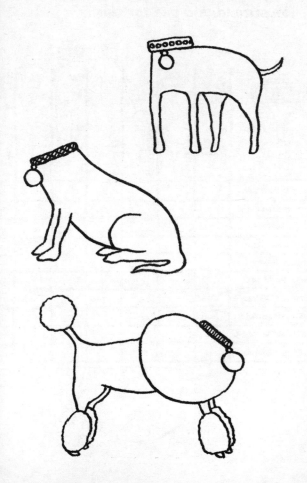

Award three points for first place, two for second and one for third

	WORKER A	WORKER B	WORKER C	WORKER D	WORKER E	WORKER F	WORKER G
MOST PUNCTUAL							
MOST PRESENTABLE							
MOST ORGANISED							
MOST MOTIVATED							
MOST CARING							
MOST POSITIVE							
MOST HELPFUL							
MOST HUMOUROUS							
MOST HARD-WORKING							
MOST GENEROUS							

YOUR STAFF AWARDS

	WORKER A	WORKER B	WORKER C	WORKER D	WORKER E	WORKER F	WORKER G
YOUR STAFF AWARDS							
MOST INTELLIGENT							
MOST DIRECT							
MOST CREATIVE							
MOST FLEXIBLE							
MOST PERSUASIVE							
MOST DEMOCRATIC							
MOST ARTICULATE							
MOST COMMITTED							
TOTAL POINTS							

Do some proper cherry picking

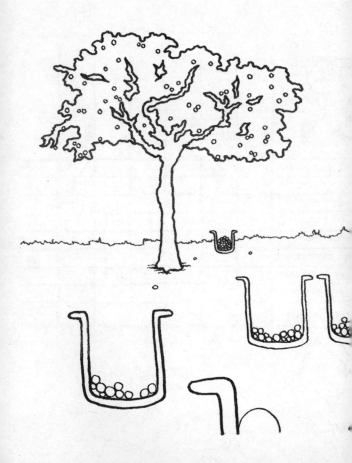

Fill in your expanding job description balloon

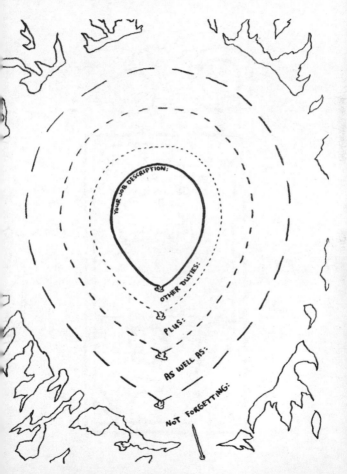

Design your own money

Executive decision maker: close your eyes and let your pen guide you

NEVER MIND

BACK OFF

READ YOUR HOROSCOPE

SLEEP ON IT

DOODLE SOME MORE

STREA

BUY

REASSESS

GO BACK TWO STEPS

PULL YOUR SOCKS UP

MAKE TIME

USE A NEW APPROACH

TRY AGAIN

ADD EXTRA CHILLI

DEFINATEL

ESCAPE NOW

IT WILL NEVER WORK

SELL

REVENGE

NO

GET A NEW HAIRCUT

BOOK FLIGHT

PHONE HOME

PICK A NEW PAGE

PRETEND THAT YOU ARE ILL

FIGHT ON

FORGO IT

BOOK FLIGHTS

DON'T WAIT

TURN TO DRUGS

RETEND THAT YOU ARE ILL

SWEAR ALOT

COLD CALL

FIGHT ON

FORGET IT

YES

FOLLOW THE PATTERN

DON'T GO BACK

ASK FOR A PAY RISE

HIDE IN THE TOILETS

OK

UH HUH

CONSULT A STRANGER

RESIGN

GOOD IDEA

BEST OF 3

NO MAYO ☺

CALL A MEETING

RETAIL THERAPY

NO

START AGAIN

DELEGATE

BOOK A TABLE

KEEP GOING

SUGGEST ALTERNATIVES

ASK AN EXPERT

A SAFE BET

DON'T EVEN GO THERE

DEFINITELY !

FINISH IT TOMORROW

See your week in pies:
one slice = one hour

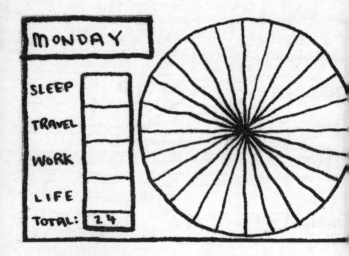

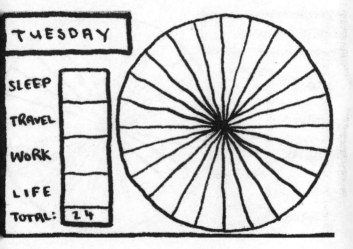

See your week in pies:
one slice = one hour

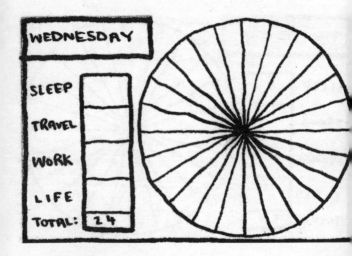

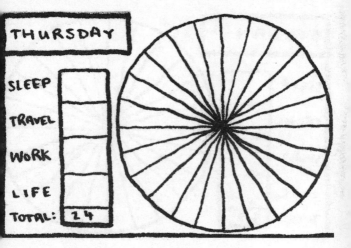

THURSDAY

SLEEP

TRAVEL

WORK

LIFE

TOTAL: 24

See your week in pies:
one slice = one hour

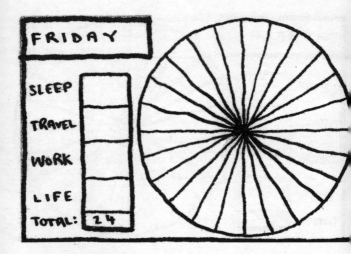

FRIDAY

SLEEP

TRAVEL

WORK

LIFE

TOTAL: 24

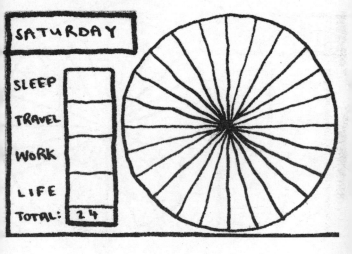

SATURDAY

SLEEP

TRAVEL

WORK

LIFE

TOTAL: 24

See your week in pies:
Sunday... take the day off

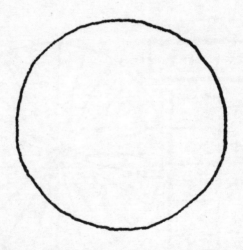

Load your gun with highlighter ink and
defend the office from hostile takeover

Meet your targets

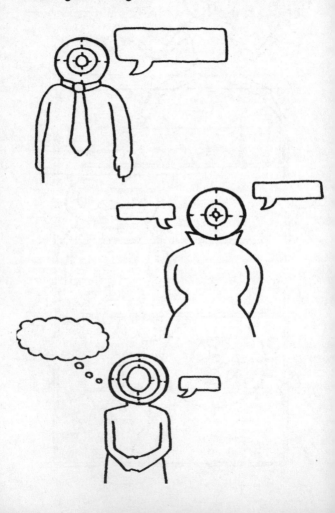

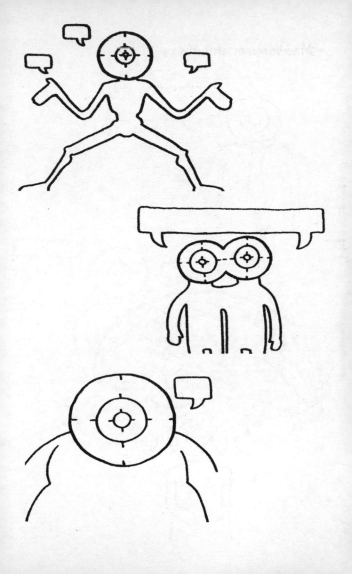

Brainstorm this page

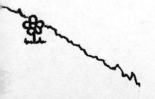

Design a month of wacky ties

WEEK 1:

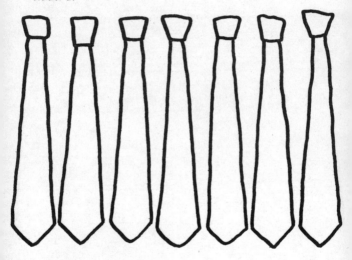

WEEK 2:

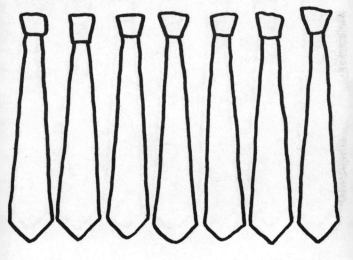

Design a month of wacky ties

WEEK 3:

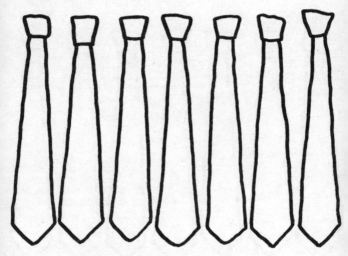

WEEK 4:

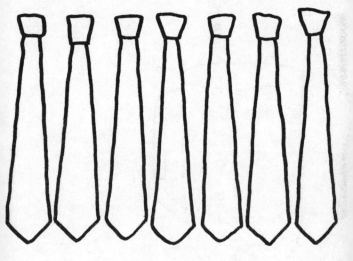

What's left after you have liquidated all your assets?

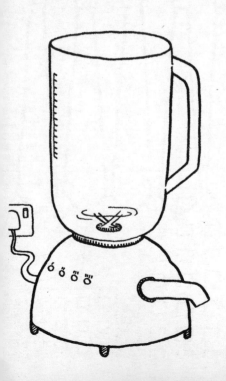

Draw some bubbles in the watercooler

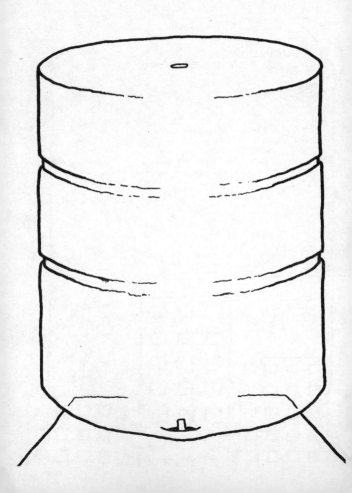

Go scuba diving in the watercooler

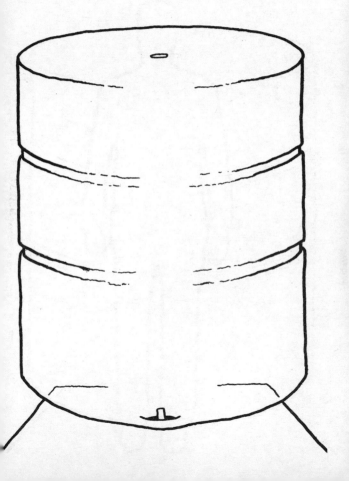

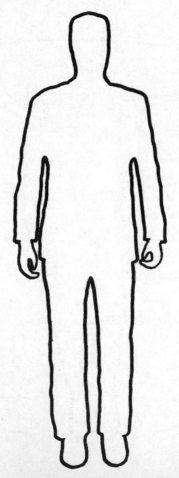

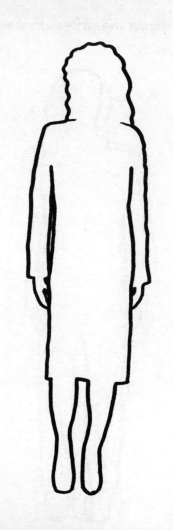

Pin the tail on the office donkey...

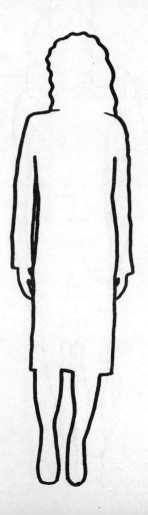

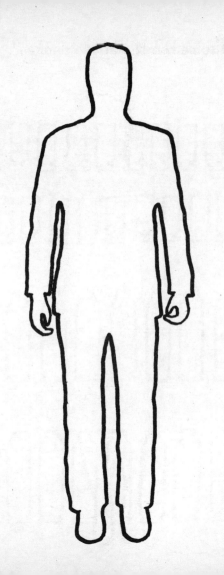

Add some bullet points

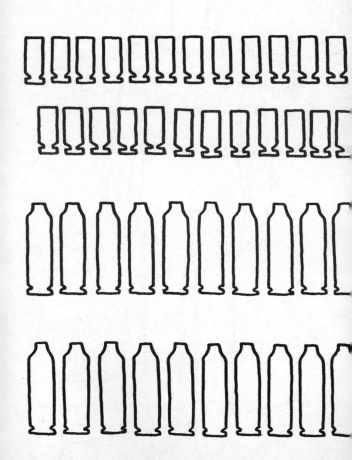

OMG, who's lunchbox is this?

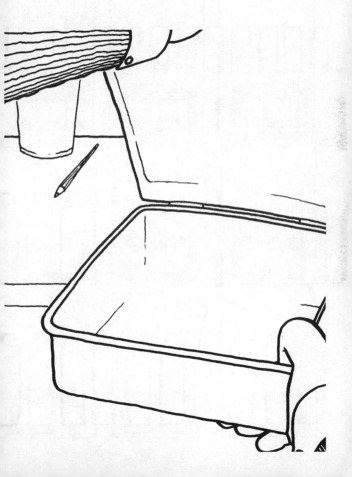

Fill the team's trophy cabinet

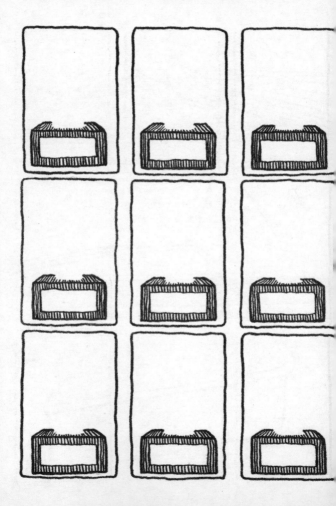

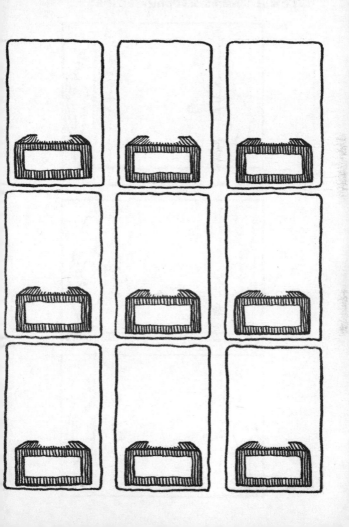

Draw in the middleman

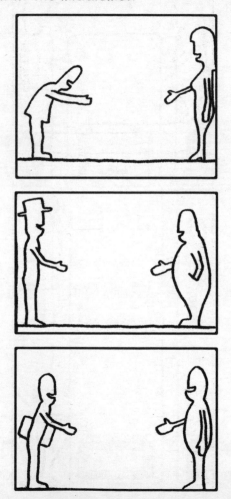

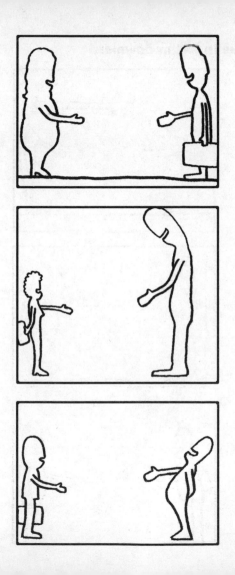

What is rolling downhill?

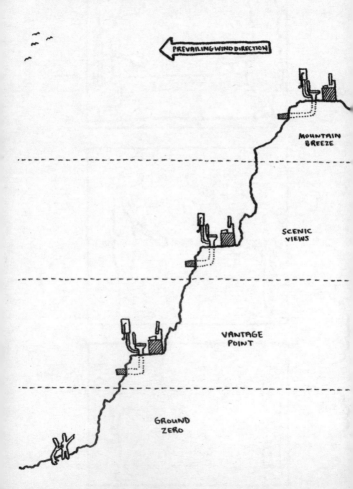

What thoughts are really outside the box?

What messages would you like to get?

Cut-out-and-keep Carriage Clock

Bail your team out . . . but be careful
what they land on

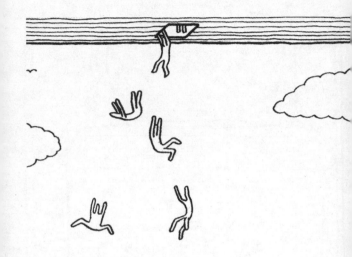

Design more bugs for your computer

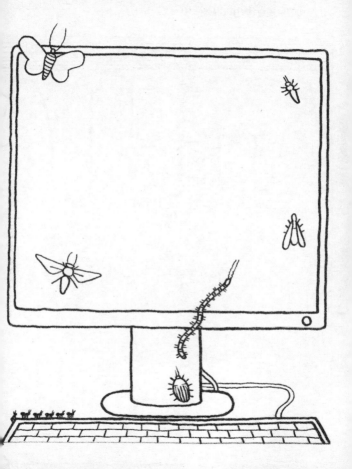

What's at the end of the line
you are towing?

Lace up and reboot your computer

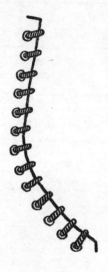

The junk mail wall of fame

Draw as many health and safety violations as possible

Draw your ultimate office party

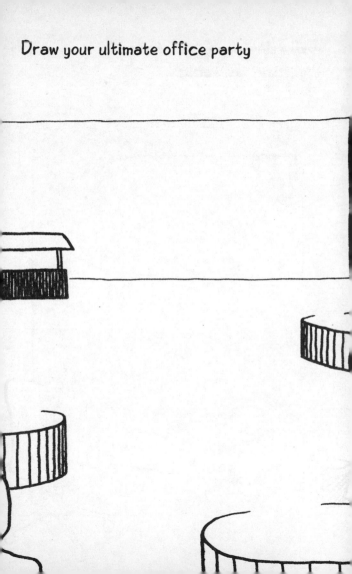

What's stopping you from getting the sack?

What happens when you get fired?

Lay your big idea on the table

Who would you employ? Complete each applicant's picture and tick to accept them

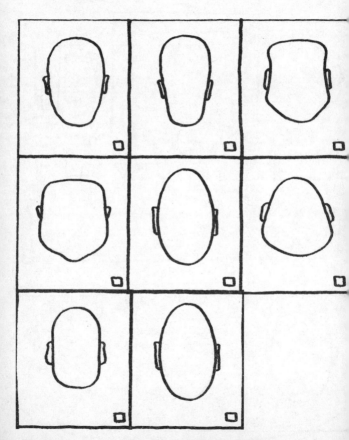

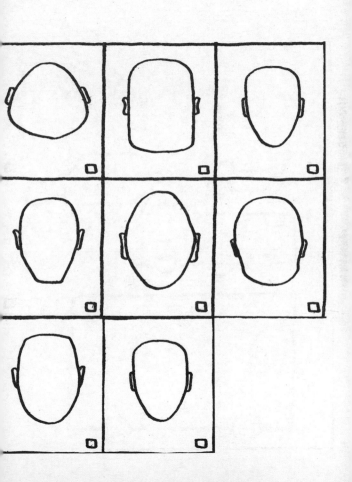

It's rush hour: how many bodies can you cram in each mode of transport?

Decorate your slice of the cake

Draw what you would like to see out of the nearest office window

Rate your enjoyment of each day and plot your Happy Graph

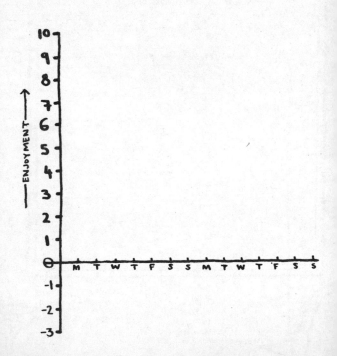

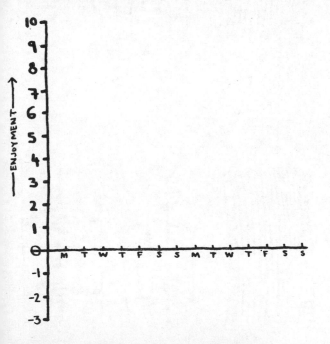

	M	T	W	T	F	S	S
WEEK 3:							
WEEK 4:							
WEEK 5:							

Make both ends meet

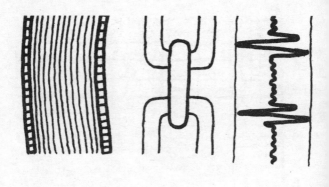

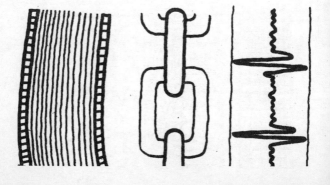

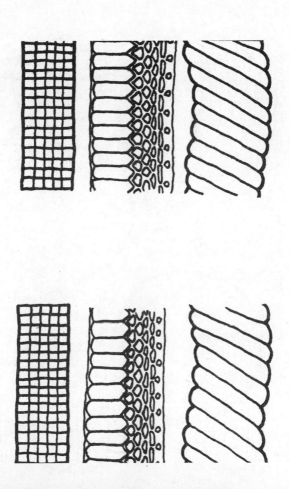

Make the biscuits look delicious

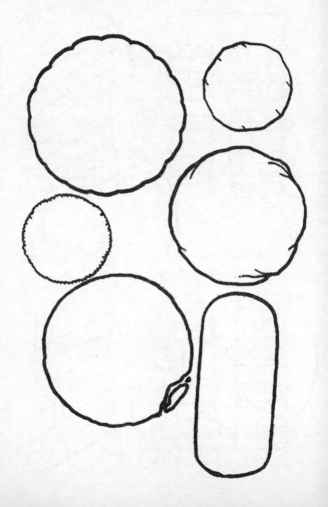

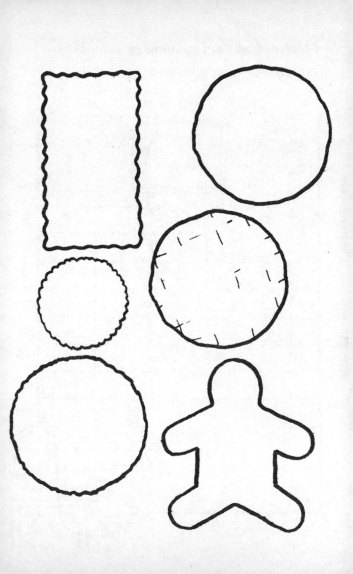

Mark off each day on your prison wall year planner

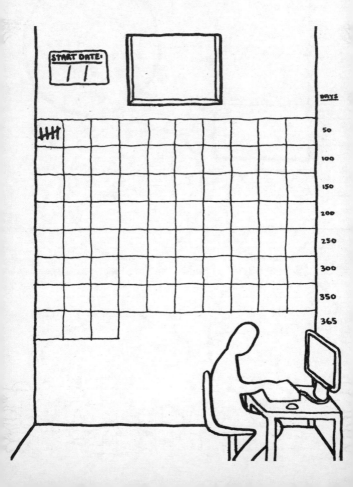

Are the mice eating the big cheese?

Please complete the Bored @ Work
diagnosis sheet

DATA COMA (i am in a) ☐

DUVET COMMITMENTS (i have periodic) ☐

OBJECT MISUSE (regular patterns of) ☐

NUTRITION DIVERSIONS (i take) ☐

TELEPHONIC ALLERGIES (i experience) ☐

STRESS FRACTURES (i have multiple) ☐

BOTTOMLESS INBOX (i have a) ☐

MALIGNANT MANAGEMENT (a case of) ☐

KEYBOARD BOXING (i train in) ☐

CONCENTRATION LAPSE (....look! a pen!) ☐

FOGHORN THROAT (i suffer from) ☐

GHOST TEAM (i am surrounded by a) ☐

TECHNICAL HITCHES (i am covered in) ☐

EXPECTATION CEILING (i have reached my) ☐

PRINTER MAGNETISM (i have daily) ☐

OPTION PARALYSIS (i have) ☐

UNOFFICIAL RESEARCH" (i conduct) ☐

FLAPPING MOUTH (i have bouts of) ☐

WINDOW FIXATING (i find myself) ☐

OVERWORKED (i am) ☐

UNDERPAID (i am) ☐

Which automated device is Dave caught in?

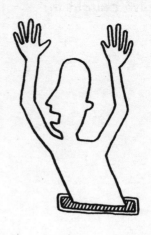

What's happened to Dave?

Groundhog Day: make each day different

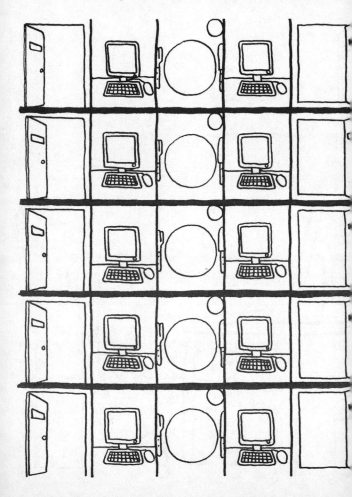

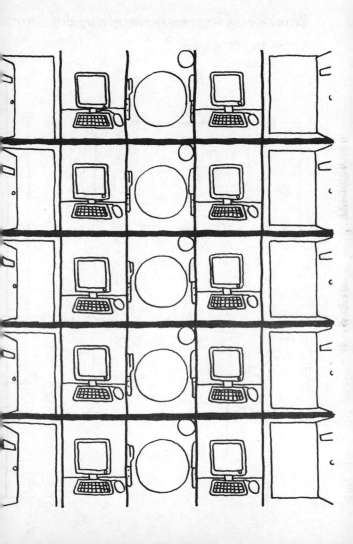

What would happen if the cleaner didn't come in for a year?

You decide what is on each floor

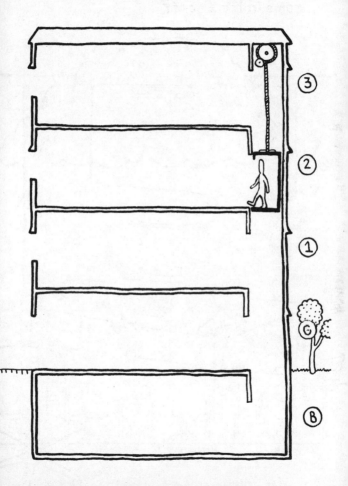

Complete the cycle of illness

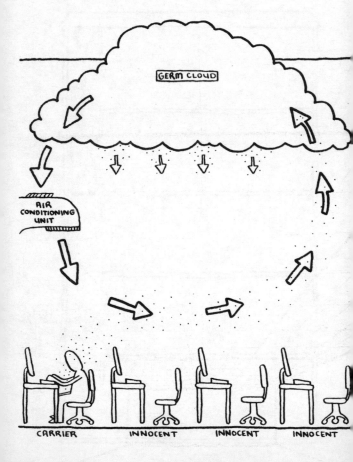

Make a chessboard on the ceiling tiles

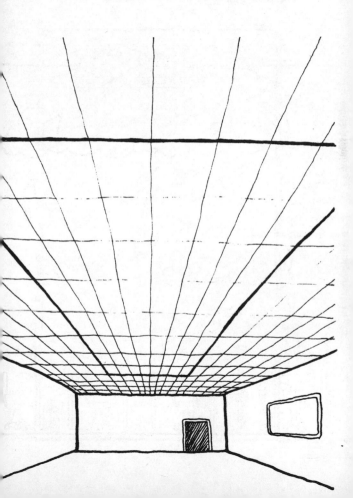

Who's in charge of all the honey that the worker bees have made?

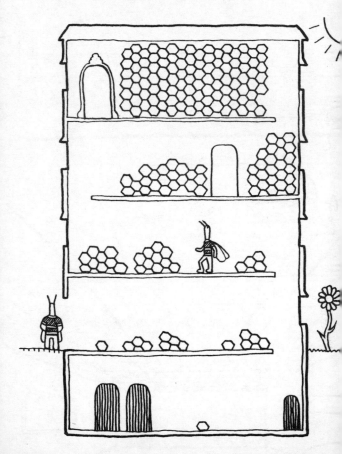

Defend your desk from invasion

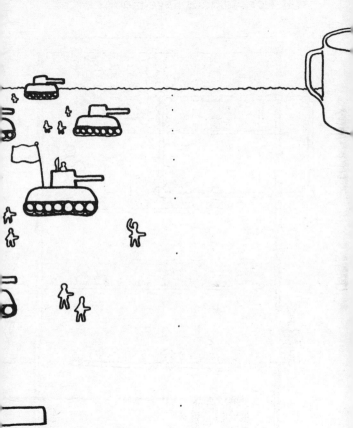

What has been left for you in reception?

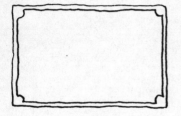

Who made your printer jam?

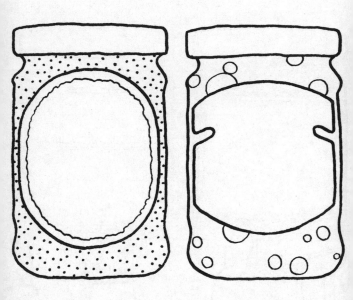

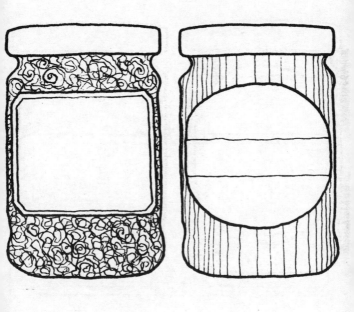

Keep yourself busy -
tidy your in and out trays

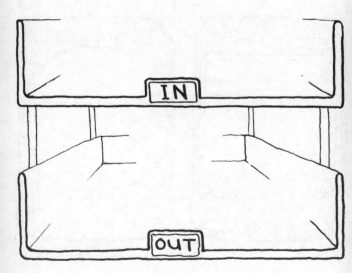

Redundancy - who's in, who's out?

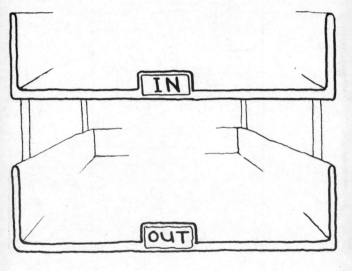

What grows in the office?

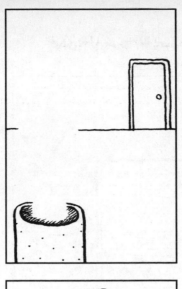

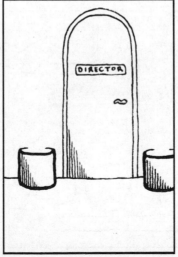

Accountability: point the finger of blame

Go with the flow

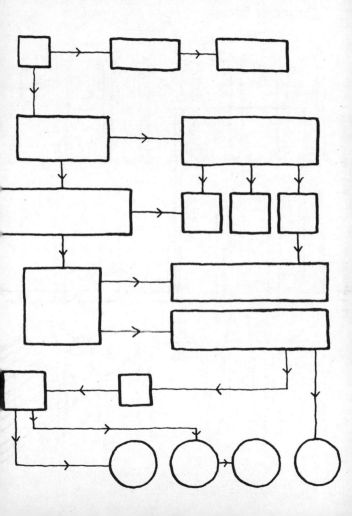

How badly do you bite your nails?

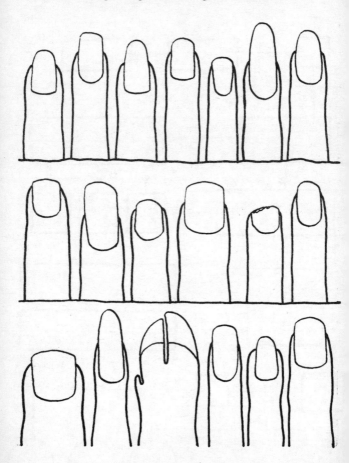

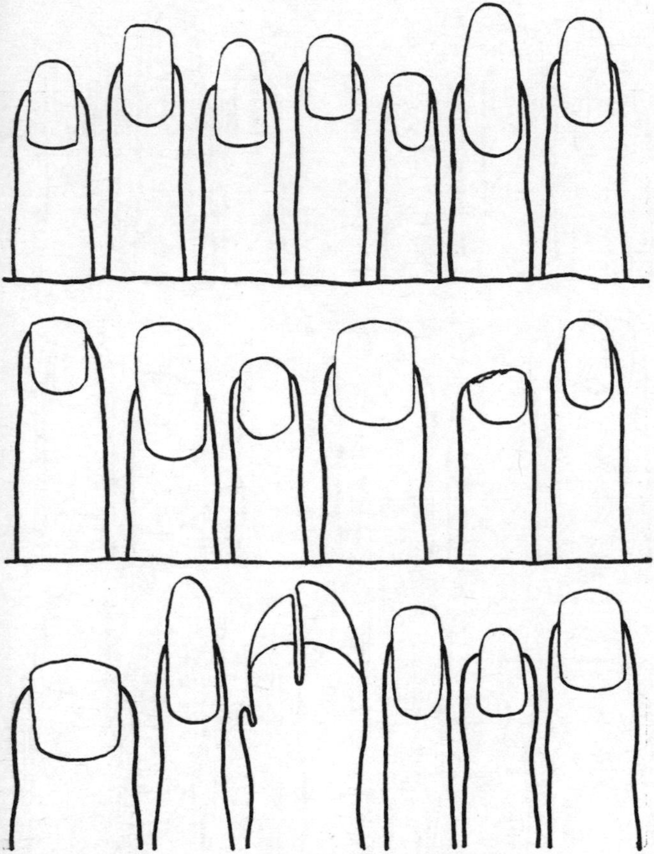

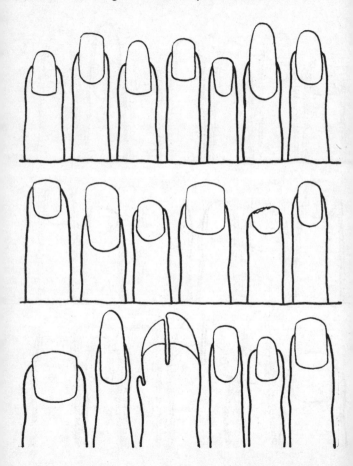

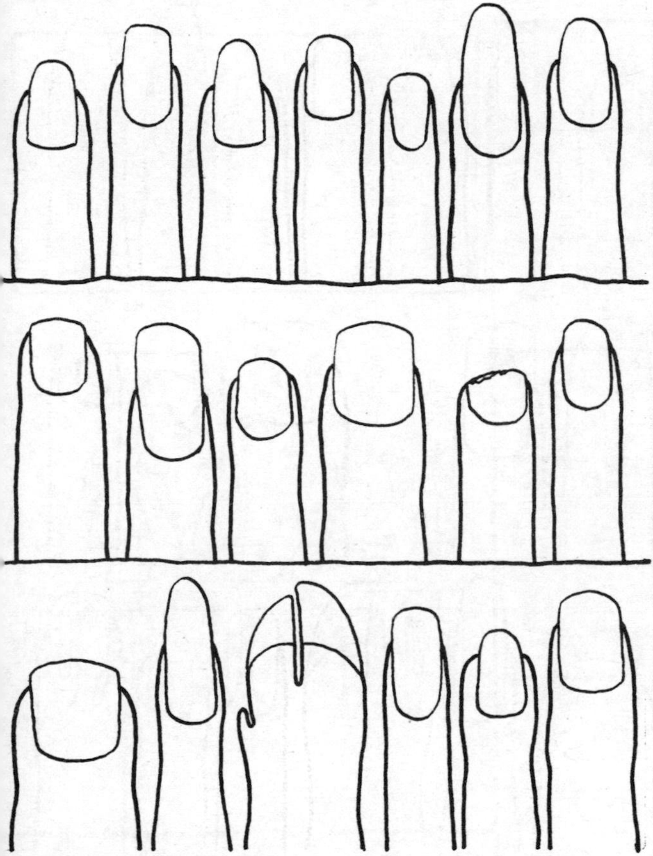

Give your resignation presentation

Add some rungs to the career ladders

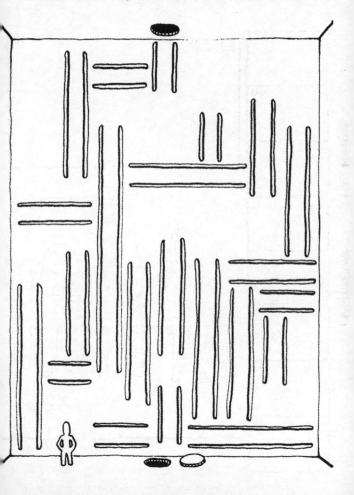

How do you look after number one?

Avoid the bullcrap, brand the cashcows and escape on the gravy train

Do your own photocopying!

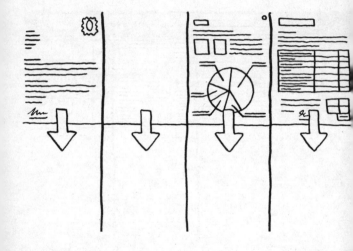

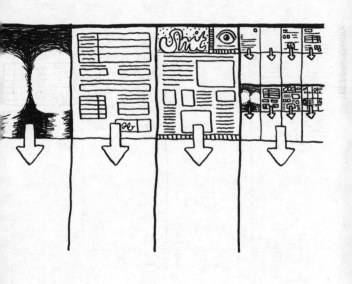

How can you adapt to the desk job?

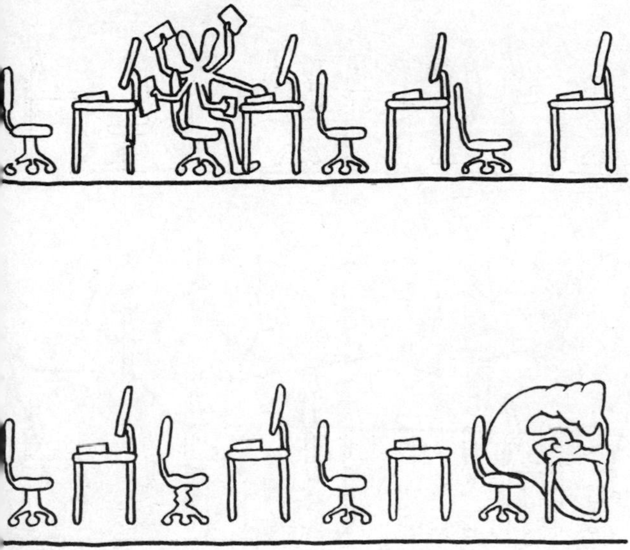

Who exactly is in the same boat as you?
Where is everyone else?

What are you daydreaming of?

What's inside the work bags, and who do they belong to?

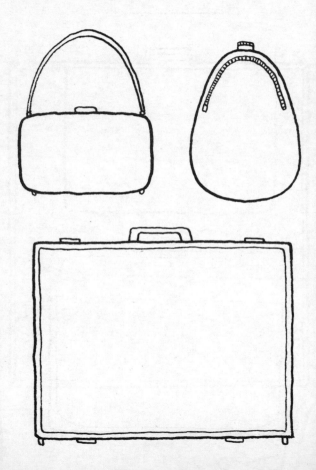

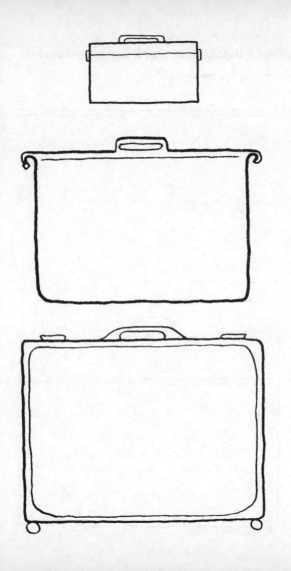

Draw your own motivational poster

SUCCESS

Discredit your colleague,
and you will shine.

Know the competition/know yourself

	BIRTHDAY	LOVED ONES	INTERESTS	☆ MY RATING
WORKER A:				
WORKER B:				
WORKER C:				
WORKER D:				
WORKER E:				
WORKER F:				
WORKER G:				

Add to these office viewpoints
(corridor, desk, keyboard, clock)

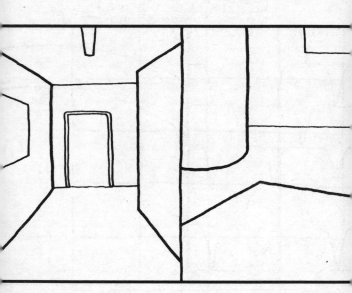

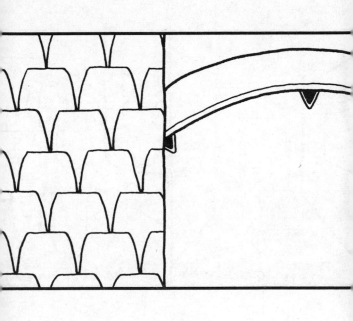

Where are you in the field of employment?

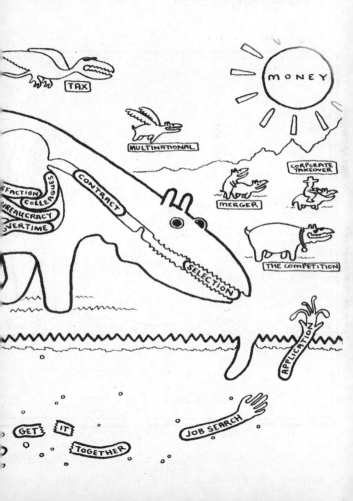

Draw the person you'd really like to see right now

Draw your dream lunch

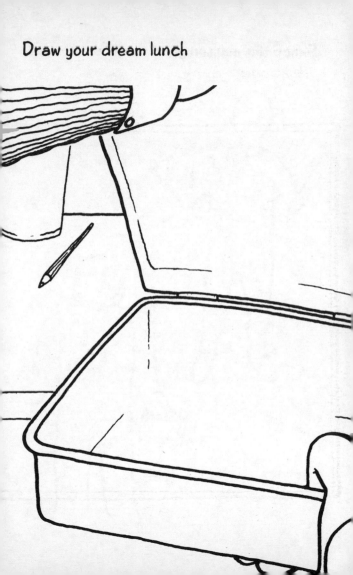

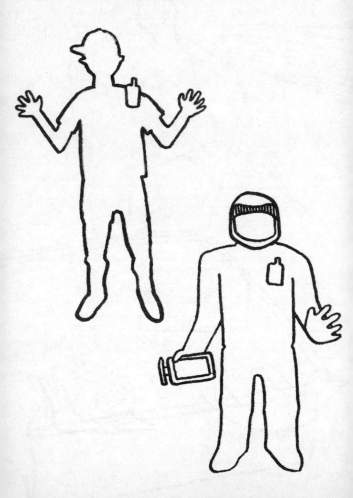

Shoot the messenger

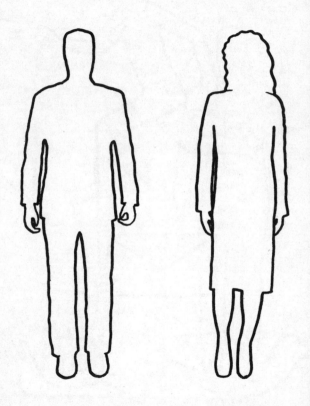

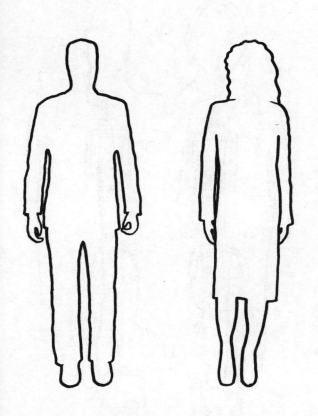

Plug in and stay connected to work

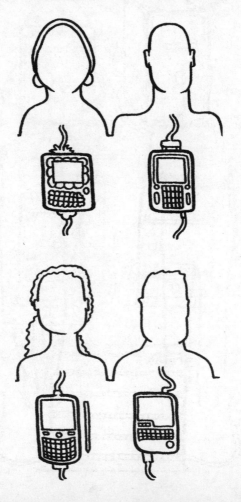

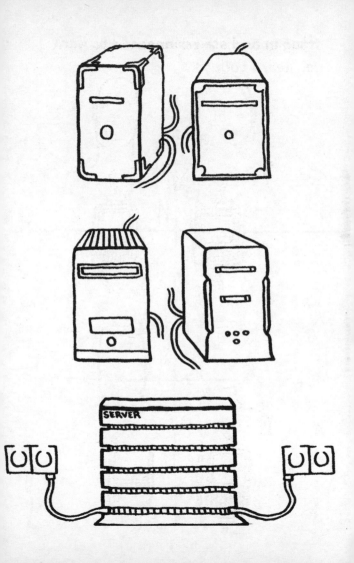

What corporate nonsense have you heard today?

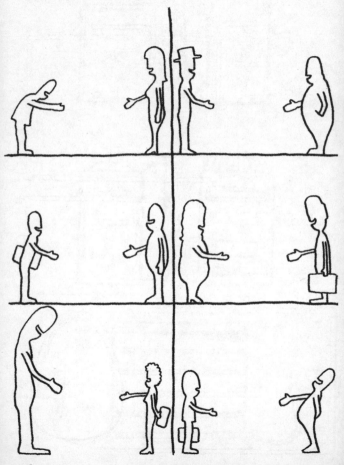

What's being sneaked out of the office?

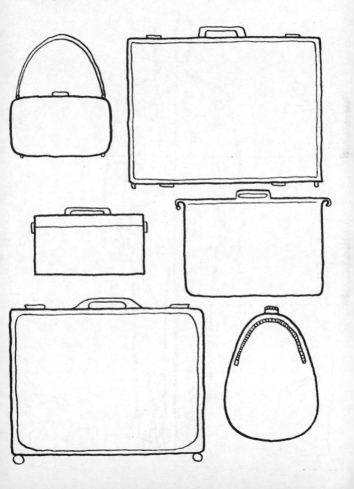

Decorate your boss in fancy dress

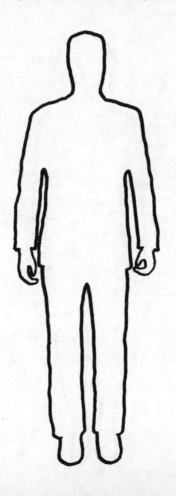

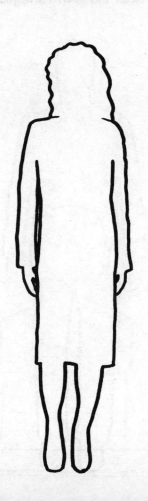

Help multitask with extra limbs

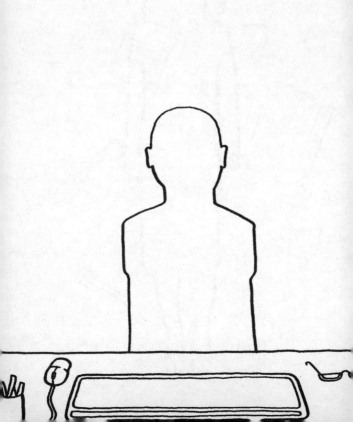

Draw your dream location...

...where would you rather be?

Plot your weekly productivity

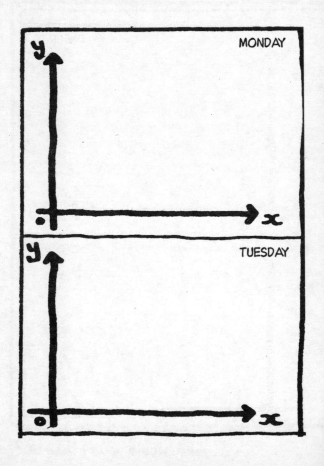

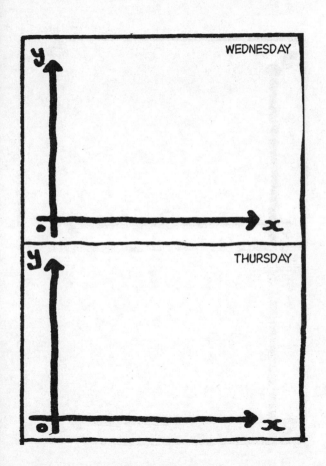

Plot your weekly productivity

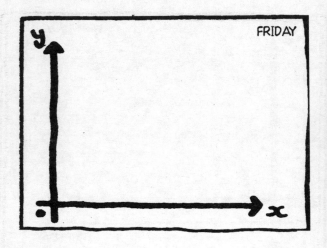

Draw the movie poster of your work life

Draw yourself walking out the door

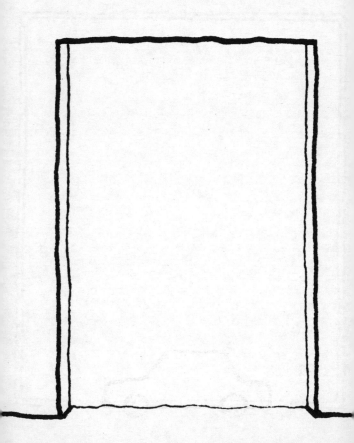

What would your dream
commute home look like?

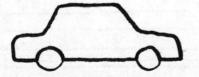

Things you have learned today

<u>Certificate of Completion</u>
Awarded to

_____

For outstanding contributions to the
Bored@Work Doodle Book

You have excelled in the following areas:

_____

_____

_____ and _____

These skills will serve you well.
Good Work.

SIGNED _Rose Adders_

DATE _____